Glen **Mice** Eddie **Bones** Derek **Hopper** **Swan** Rooks **Corgi** Blount

Degus Rodman Ruben **Bat**terson Nick "The **Chick**" Van **Eggshell**

Cedric Ce**bull**os Jon **Bear**y Jerome Ker**Sea Turtle Kangaroo**meal Robinson

Shea **Seals Seagull** Threatt Anthony "**Pig**" Miller George **Finch Frog**gy King Fred **Rabbits Deer**ek Strong

Anthony **Squealer Lobster** Conner Randolph **Caws** Kurt **Ram**bis Lloyd **Spaniel**s **Ram** Bowie **Pony** Smith

Antonio **Hare**vey **Beaver** Wilson **Duck** Christie Reggie Jordan Danny **Shells** James **Wool**thy Sam **Purr**kins

A.C. **Green-Vine-Snake Jay**mes Edwards Benoit **Bunny**jamin Duane **Cougar** Al-**Eggs** Blackwell

Jackrabbit Haley Demetrius **Cowlip** Rory **Sparrow** Terry **Beagle** Keith **Crow**ens Cliff Ro**bison** Larry **Flew**

Furving Thomas **Bear**vin "**Magic**" Johnson **Woodchuck**y Brown Tony **Bruin** Mychal **Chomp**son

Jawann Old**ham Bluejay** Vincent **Shark** McNamara **Mule** McCants Michael **Cougar** Orlando **Wool**ridge

Mink Higgins Steve **Buck**nall David **River Snakes** Jeff **Lamb Camel** Abdul-Jabbar **Billygoat** Thompson

Tony Camp**bull Mink** Smrek Milt **Wagner Stingray** Tolbert Wes **Mammoth**ews Pétur Karl Guð**mouse**son

Frank Brick**cow**ski **Egg**rian Branch **Woodchuck** Nevitt Jerome **Hammerhead**erson **Hairy** Spriggs

Maurice **Locust** Mike **McGeese Munch** Kupchak Ronnie **Lobster Bobcat** McAdoo **Squirrel** Jones

Ja**maul** Wilkes Irwin **Egg** Fletcher aka FLETCH, he's actually six-five, with the afro six-nine **Cow**vin Garrett

Egggie Jordan **Swan** Nater **Billygoat** Ray Bates **Claw** Johnson **Flight** Jones Joe **Cougar Swarm** Nixon

Shark Landsberger Steve **Mink**s **Swim** Brewer Kevin Mc**Kennel** Alan **Herd**y Butch **Flea Mule**s Patrick

Dog Ford Brad **Howl**and Butch **Garter Snake** Jim Chones aka **Bunny** Tony **Jackal**son **Kennel** Carr

Marty **Birds Owl**iver Mack Ron **Bone** Spencer Hay**woodchuck Egg**rian Dantley Brad Ear**nest** Davis

Earl **Ate 'Em Dove** Robisch Jim **Mice Flew** Hudson Ron **Garter Snake** Charlie **Scottish Terrier Dog** Chaney

Ernie Di**Growl**gorio Kermit "**The Frog**" Washington Tom A-**barn-owl**-nethy **Owl**en Murphy Bo **Llama**

Cliff **Millipede** C.J. Ku**peccary** Cazzie **Mussel Kennel** Warner Lucius **Fowl**en Mack **Cow**vin Marv **Rabbits**

John **Roach** Johnny Neu**manatee** Porky Calhoun Donnie Free**manatee Quail** Goodrich Jim Mc**Spaniel**s

Zelmo **Beetle Bat** Riley **Prawn** Williams **Moo** Lantz Walt **Weasel**y **Bull** Bridges **Bruin** Winters Stan **Lovebird**

Travis **Great Dane** Connie **Hawk**ins aka **The Hawk Shell**more Smith **Hoppy** Hairston Nate **Hawk**thorne

Mule Counts **Bull** Turner **Flyin'** Robinson Jery **Nest Swim** McMillian Roger **Bruin** Wilt Chamber**lion**

John **Bear** Trapp Keith **Earwig**son **Flea**Roy Ellis Jim **Clam**mons Earnie **Krill**um Elgin **Baler Fur**red Hetzel

John **Tarsier**vant **Rook** Roberson **Woolly** McCarter **Bull** Hewitt **Duck** Garrett Johnny **Egg**an Mike **Lynx**

Cliff-Swallow Anderson Freddie **Claw**ford **Bluejay** Carty Tom **Hawk**ins Archie **Cluck Feral (Cat)** Imhoff

Dennis **Hamilton Fur**win Mueller Jim **Barns** John **Wet Seal Flank** Finkel Jerry **Chompers Swan** Block

Illustrated by Cerise Markham
(c) 2019, Lynn Markham
Tails of Soul, Inc.
tailsofsoul.com

ISBN 978-0-578-58595-6

Printed in South Korea
First edition, November 2019

VOLUME 1: THE ULTIMATE BEDTIME FANTHOLOGY

By Lynn & Cerise Markham

Dedicated to Chick Hearn & Stu Lantz.

We used to mute the national broadcasts during the Playoffs so we could listen to Chick & Stu on the radio... even when the TV and radio weren't in synch.

Thank you for having a positive impact on the lives of millions of Laker fans!

Rest in peace, Chick.

We hope in the age of social media and anxiety that this book helps children understand the value of persevering through struggles.

"Welcome back Special Agents Chick Hearn & Moo Lantz!" Jeanie shouted excitedly. "The world's success depends on your next time travel mission."

"Holy guacamole! How can we help?" Chick asked.

"We need you to visit our Laker greats when they were kids and collect their SWAG (Sacrifice, Work, Attitude & Grit) to help teach kids and future Laker greats that EVERYONE has to work hard for success!" Jeanie continued. "Laker SWAG is the only thing that can save the world. Walk with me into the L.A.B."

DYK: Did you know that "Dr. Buss" wasn't just a nickname? Laker owner Jerry Buss received his doctorate degree in Chemistry from USC!

Dr. Jerry Buzz

JEANIE BUZZ, QUEEN BEE

"Behold the Great Western Store 'Em!" Jeanie exclaimed. "This will collect the SWAG nano particles from our Laker greats when they were kids."

"Wait… so… how is this life lesson vacuum thing going to save the world?" asked Moo.

"SIMPLE!" Jeanie Buzz shouted. "The collected nano particles will calibrate the dilithium port resistance synthesizer, reset the quantum dorsal nitrogen emitter, re-route the…"

"Huh?" Chick interrupted.

"Don't question science, gentlemen," Jeanie laughed. "Green button for collect. Red for zap. Blue for raspberry slurpees."

 The Great Western Store 'Em device is a shout out to the Great Western Forum where the Lakers played from 1967 to 1999.

"What about the Refrigerator time machine?" asked Chick.

"The Refrigerator is now voice activated. All you need to do is say the year from the player's case file, put the game in the refrigerator, and you're off!" Jeanie explained.

"Oh, and Pizza Mode is still experimental… so whatever you do… DON'T TOUCH the pizza button!"

Sneak peek at the buttons inside The Refrigerator!

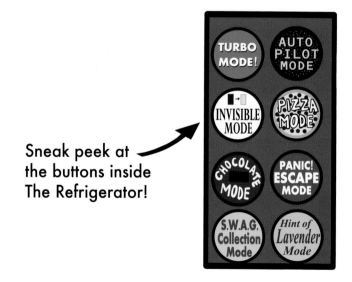

 Quick Poll: By a raise of hands, who thinks someone will touch the pizza button??

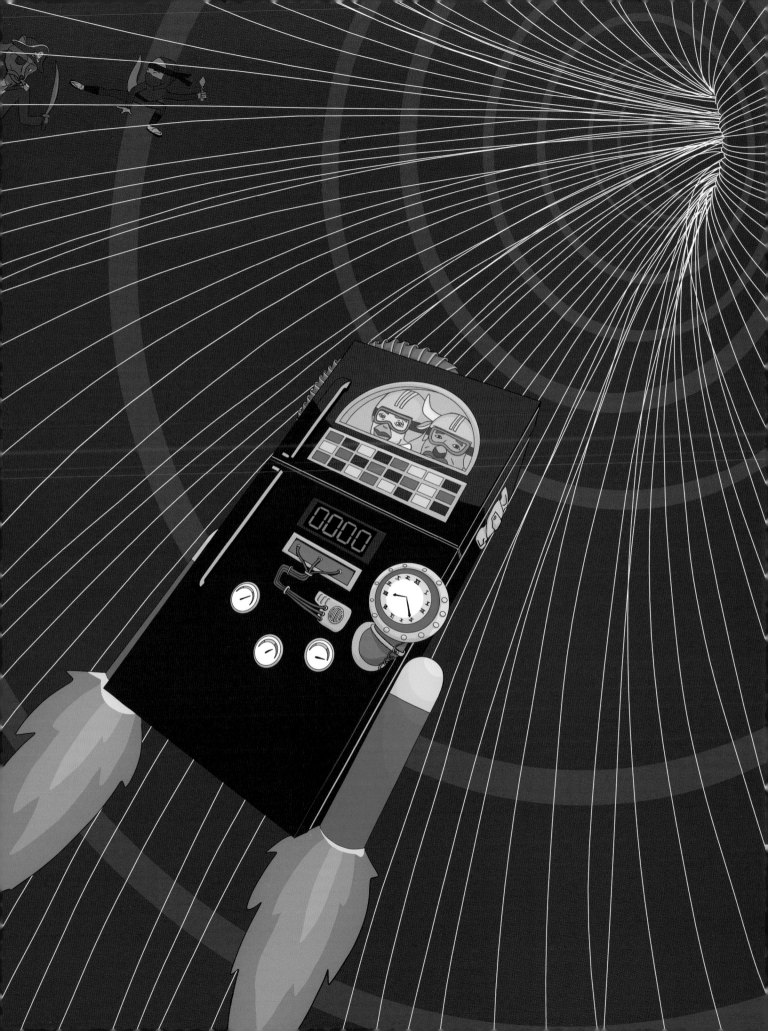

"Let's give it a whirl!" Chick exclaimed. *"This one's in the refrigerator! The lights are out! The eggs are cooling! The butter's getting hard. And the Jelloooo's jiggggglin'!"*

(MAKE MACHINE NOISES and LIGHTLY SHAKE AUDIENCE to simulate time machine booting up.)

"OOOH NOOOO!!! I forgot to say the year first!"

Chick Hearn, the greatest sports announcer of all time, used to jokingly **"put games in the Refrigerator"** by saying these silly things about eggs, butter, & jello when the Lakers were well ahead at the end of a game.

"AHHHHH SPACE MONSTERS!!!" Moo yelled.

Chick yelled the escape code as loud as chickenly possible, "THE MUSTARD IS OFF THE HOT DOG!!!"

Robot Voice: "ESCAPE MODE INITIATED."

(MAKE MACHINE NOISES and LIGHTLY SHAKE AUDIENCE to simulate time machine booting up.)

 Chick Hearn used to say, "The mustard's off the hot dog!" whenever a player messed up a play while trying to show off!

"Whew. That was a close one."

"Yep, but it's just us now," said Moo. "No more of those… AHHHHH!! SPACE MONSTER!!!"

BLORP: "BLORP BLORP BLORP! BLOOOOORP BLOOORP!"

"Where are we?" Chick wondered. "And why are we in these RIDICULOUS PIZZA SUITS?!? BLORP!! NO PIZZA BUTTON!"

"AHHH!! T-REX BIRTHDAY PARTY AND THEY THINK WE'RE THE PIZZA!!" Moo yelled.

"1946! THIS-GAME'S-IN-THE-REFRIGERATOR-THE-LIGHTS-ARE-OUT-THE-EGGS-ARE-COOLING-THE-BUTTER'S-GETTING-HARD-AND-THE-JELLO-IS-JIGGLING!!!!!"

(MAKE MACHINE NOISES and LIGHTLY SHAKE AUDIENCE to simulate time machine booting up.)

LAKERS

ELGIN HAY BALER

CONFIDENTIAL

ELGIN BALER

ALIASES: MR. INSIDE, THE RABBIT, MOTORMOUTH

READ THIS PART OF EACH REPORT OUT LOUD

Meet Elgin Baler. This stallion was THE MANE. His dunks gave moose goosebumps and his moves gave geese meesebumps.

Did you know the Lakers moved to LA from Minnesota to show Elgin Baler to the world?

It's true. This guy had it all.

FUN FACTS & JIBBER JABBER:

- Father of the spin move, double pumping, hesitation dribbles, and no look passes!
- Performed first ever *Euro Step* in early 60s*!*
- Elgin was the original Dr. J, Michael Jordan
- Had 71 points and 25 rebs. in ONE GAME
- Lakers would have gone bankrupt in 1959 without Elgin (No Elgin… no Lakers)
- Talked so much they called him *Motormouth*

TIME TRAVEL OPTIONS:

1945 – Washington DC

1955 – Caldwell, Idaho

1956 – Seattle, Washington

1959 – Minneapolis, Minnesota

Elgin didn't have it all growing up in Washington D.C.

He wanted a basketball so badly he could taste it, but his family didn't have a lot of money. He was grateful even when all they could afford was a tennis ball.

He pretended that his tennis ball was a basketball and dribbled it ALL. DAY. LONG. He didn't have a hoop so he just visualized a hoop and practiced shooting against the wall!

No basketball. No hoop. No pouting.

 Thinking cap! Discuss what the following saying means to you: "It doesn't matter what happens to you. It's how you deal with it."

CONFIDENTIAL

JERRY NEST

ALIASES: THE LOGO, MR. CLUTCH, MR. OUTSIDE

Jerry Nest never stopped never stopping until he brought a championship to LA!

He also never stopped getting sweet nicknames: The Logo. ~~The Beak from Cabin Creek~~. Mr. Outside. Mr. Clutch.

NOT FROM CABIN CREEK

Why Mr. Clutch? Because he would make **60 FOOT SHOTS** at the buzzer! In the Finals!

FUN FACTS & JIBBER JABBER:

- Champion, Finals MVP
- Basically *The Godfather* of the Lakers
- Helped Lakers win 11 championships as player, GM, VP (and *other stuff)
- They used his silhouette to make the league logo… hence the nickname "The Logo"
- If they had three pointers in the 1960s… Jerry would have been MVP every year
- Insanely competitive. Insanely nice hair.

*Other stuff = residual benefits from his work drafting Kobe and signing Shaq

TIME TRAVEL OPTIONS:

1948 – Chelyan, West Virginia

1952 – Chelyan, West Virginia

1955 – East Bank, West Virginia

1958 – Morgantown, West Virginia

Young Jerry Nest didn't whine or pout when he got cut from the football and baseball teams. That skinny little bird went into full BEAK MODE like Marshawn Finch to make the basketball team.

When it rained, he dribbled in the mud. When it snowed, he practiced with gloves on. No excuses.

 Jerry West didn't have a hoop as a kid. His neighbors let him shoot on the hoop on their old shed. We have tremendous respect for Jerry West.

Jerry Nest made a promise to his older brother that he'd be the best player ever from West Virginia. Young Jerry was crushed when his brother died in the Korean War.

Nothing in the world was going to stop Jerry from keeping his promise to his brother. He practiced so hard everyday that his feathers would fall out.

 In the story we have his feathers falling out since he's a bird, but in real life young Jerry West practiced so hard that his fingers would bleed. He kept his promise. Kids need to learn about Jerry West's dedication!

The Big Dipper

PHIL JACKALSON, FUTURE ALL TIME GREAT LAKER COACH, GETTING HIS SHOT DESTROYED BY WILT.

LAKERS 13

TOP SECRET

Wilt Chamberlion, Center

WILT CHAMBERLION

ALIASES: THE BIG DIPPER, WILT THE STILT, GOLIATH

Wilt Chamberlion was super tall and super strong.

He was so amazing that he scored 100 points in *one game!*

He was so tough that he helped the Lakers win the Finals with a broken wrist!

Wilt wasn't scared of anything.

BLOOOOORP!
YOUR PIZZA SAUCE LEFT A STAIN!
NO MORE PIZZA BUTTON!!!

FUN FACTS & JIBBER JABBER:

- Champion, MVP, Finals MVP
- 100 points in one game! Averaged 50 points & 25 rebs for season!
- Only Wilt and the doctors knew he was playing in the 1972 Finals with a broken wrist (everyone thought it was sprained) – had 24 points, 29 rebounds, 8 assists, and 8 blocks in Game 5!
- Dominated track & field - sprints, high jump, triple jump, and shot put!
- Wilt was inducted into the Volleyball Hall of Fame. True story.
- Turned down Red Auerbach and the Celtics as a high schooler! Coach Auerbach tried to convince Wilt to go to college in Boston so he could use a "territorial pick" to get him (60s thing to give local teams "first dibs" to get local guys to boost fan interest). Wilt told Red and the Celtics, "No thanks." Atta boy. True Laker.

TIME TRAVEL OPTIONS:

1945 – Philadelphia, Pennsylvania

1952 – Philadelphia, Pennsylvania

1954 – Thompson, New York

1957 – Lawrence, Kansas

Young Wilt was scared.

He was scared of going to school. He was scared of being different. He was almost twice the size of everyone else in Mrs. Cowabungalow's 4th grade class and he hated it!

Kids called him names he didn't like - Goliath, Wilt the Stilt, Dr. Lankenstein, Skyscraper, or Tree boy. This was a hard time.

 Our son asked if it was really hard for the sloth guy (picking his nose) to tag other kids during recess. Also, can you spot the two animals getting "bunny ears" in this class photo?

Wilt's family was silly and gave him nicknames too! But they made sure to pick ones he liked.

They called him "The Big Dipper" since he was so tall he had to dip his head under the door each time. He loved that nickname.

"Once Wilt's family helped him learn that it's okay to be different, he really dominated!"

"That's right, Chick. Whoooo eeeee yooowza magooowza!!!"

Thinking Cap! Do you know any kids who are getting picked on or called names? What can you do to help? You can stick up for them! And be their friend!

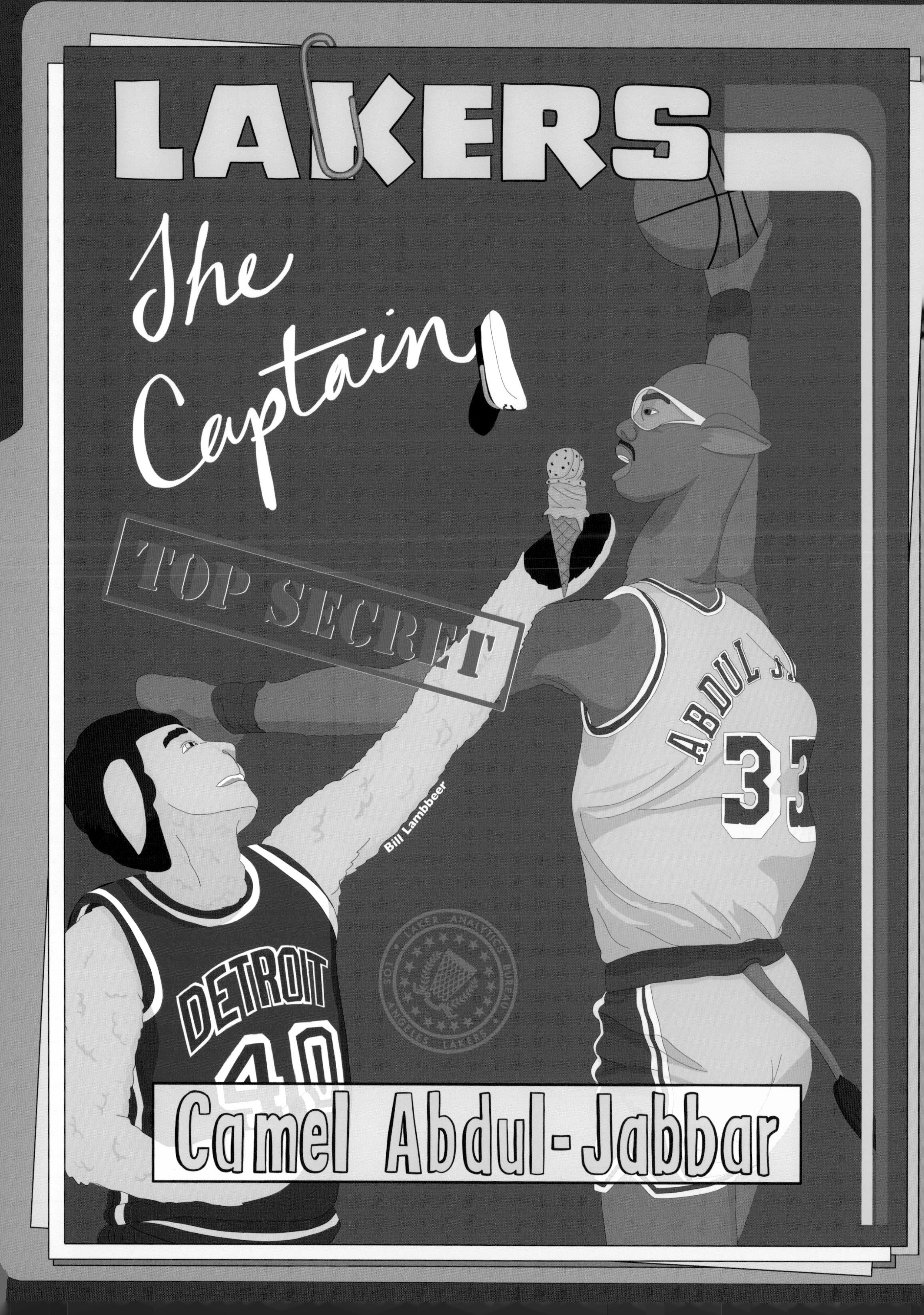
LAKERS
The Captain
TOP SECRET
33
Bill Lambbeer
DETROIT
40
LAKER ANALYTICS BUREAU
LOS ANGELES LAKERS
Camel Abdul-Jabbar

CONFIDENTIAL

CAMEL ABDUL-JABBAR

ALIASES: CAPTAIN, CAP, THE TOWER FROM POWER, LEW ALCINDOR

O Captain! My Captain! Camel Abdul Jabbar was the ultimate boss way before kids could floss.

Try to block his shot? **BOOM. Skyhook.**

Try to push him around? **BOOM. Skyhook.**

Try to distract him with mint chocolate chip ice cream like Bill Lambbeer of the Baa'aa'aad Boys? He'll take a bite, but still... **BOOM. SKYHOOOOOK!**

FUN FACTS & JIBBER JABBER:

- Champion, MVP, Finals MVP
- Most points & MVPs ever (6 MVPs!!!)
- Had the sweetest shot of all time – The Skyhook
- His goggles are widely considered the GGOAT – greatest goggles of all time
- Was really into yoga way before yoga was a thing
- Appeared in the second greatest movie about airplanes ever made
- Fought Bruce Lee (in a movie, but still)

TIME TRAVEL OPTIONS:

1956 – Cornwell Heights, Pennsylvania

1958 – Brooklyn, New York

1964 – New York, New York

1968 – Los Angeles, California

Camel Abdul Jabbar was so tall in 5th grade that he played against 8th graders like Swan Claude Van Damme and Giraffrey Von Schnozzleberger. "The Schnozz" blocked his shot back in his face every time.

Instead of whining or quitting, Camel started practicing the hook shot everyday so he could shoot it over the older kids!

"And just like that, Chick, the sweet, sweet baby **Skyhook was born**!"

"Yeah, Moo. The Skyhook's great, but THE TIME MACHINE IS OVERFLOWING WITH PIZZA!!! BLOOOORP!!! STOP. TOUCHING. THE PIZZA BUTTON!! NO MORE PIZZA DANCE PARTIES!!!!"

 Many people don't know that Kareem's unstoppable Skyhook shot was born from his struggles as a 5th grader. What if Kareem just gave up?!?

Camel Abdul-Jabbar was dunking on so many animals in college that the old guys made a rule that NOBODY was allowed to slam dunk for TEN YEARS!

Camel could have pouted, but instead he perfected the Skyhook to win three college championships!

 The rule change is a true story! They changed the rules to try to slow him down. Didn't work. Also, Kareem was born "Ferdinand Lewis Alcindor" and was known as "Lew Alcindor" until changing his name in the early 70s.

CONFIDENTIAL

BEARVIN JOHNSON

ALIASES: MAGIC, BUCK, EJ THE DJ, THE MAGIC MAN

EVERYONE wanted to be Magic Johnson. Even David Hasselhog. Magic didn't hassle The Hog, but he couldn't resist making the Celtics look silly.

Laser pass through Larry Bird's legs? *Dish*.

Baby hook over Kevin McQuail and Robert Bearish for the win? *Swish*.

Fastbreak with James Woolthy and Byron Trot? *Delish*.

With Magic, it was SHOWTIME for the Lakers.

FUN FACTS & JIBBER JABBER:

- Champion, MVP, Finals MVP
- Has the best nickname of all time – "Magic"
- Tallest point guard and greatest passer ever
- Ended the Boston – Lakers curse
- His afro in high school would've made even Ben Wallace jealous (Seriously. Google it.)
- Inspired middle aged guys with names like Melvin in places like Huntington Beach to wear Magic Johnson jersey aprons every time they made waffles

TIME TRAVEL OPTIONS:

1967 – Lansing, Michigan

1969 – Lansing, Michigan

1979 – East Lansing, Michigan

1984 – Los Angeles, California

Before Showtime, it was SHOVEL TIME.

Magic wanted to be the best and he worked for it EVERY. SINGLE. DAY.

No crowds. No lights. No high fives. No pats on the back. No hibernating. Just snow. Cold. Stiff paws. And lots of practice.

 Magic is known for Showtime, but he grew up in a blue collar home in Lansing, Michigan where he shoveled snow to be able to practice basketball in the winter. Also, our son asked if his family was hibernating in this picture.

Magic never stopped practicing. He dribbled to school everyday. He even dribbled when he went to the store for his mom. He dribbled there with his right paw...

Then he dribbled home
with his left paw.

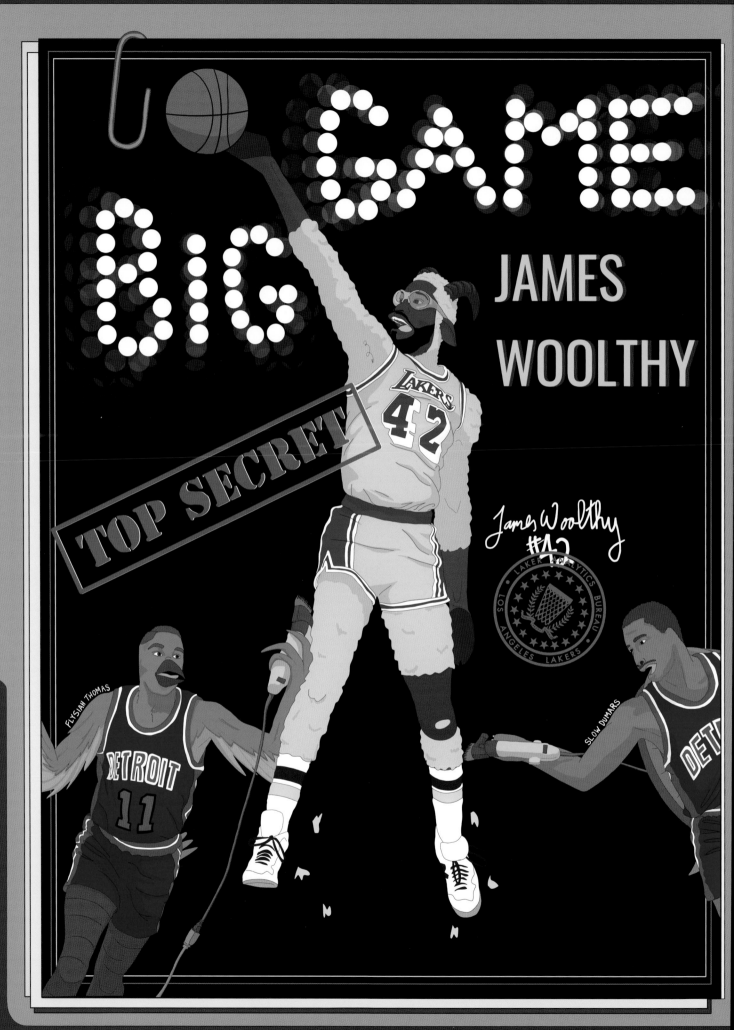

JAMES WOOLTHY

ALIASES: BIG GAME JAMES, CLEVER, J-DUB, ICE MAN

CONFIDENTIAL

James Woolthy always heated up in the biggest games. Detroit and Boston would try to shear his wool in The Finals to cool him down, but it never worked. He always dominated. That's why they called him "Big Game James."

FUN FACTS & JIBBER JABBER:

- Champion, Finals MVP
- This sheep was one baa'aaad lamba jamma
- Dove out of bounds to save ball & 1987 Finals – the replay still gives fans the chills every time
- Dominated Boston and Detroit
- Definitely pulled off wearing goggles
- Great Klingon? Or Greatest Klingon? (Big Game was a Klingon on Star Trek)

TIME TRAVEL OPTIONS:

1971 – Gastonia, North Carolina

1977 – Gastonia, North Carolina

1982 – Chapel Hill, North Carolina

1987 – Los Angeles, California

Growing up he was just "Little Game James."

James Woolthy was fragile and weak as a kid. His two brothers were much older and stronger than him and thought he would never become a great player.

His life changed when he saw a poster about scholarships.

James' parents worked until 9pm many nights to support their family. James was grateful for them as he ate dinner alone.

James wanted to save his parents money so he didn't stop until he got a basketball scholarship from the University of North Carolina. He even won the college championship as the MVP with his buddies Sam Purrrkins and Mibhael ("my-bull") Jordan.

 James Worthy was driven to greatness by a love for his parents and a desire to help the family financially. What can we learn from Big Game James' example? Also, he was the best player on a team that had Michael Jordan!!!

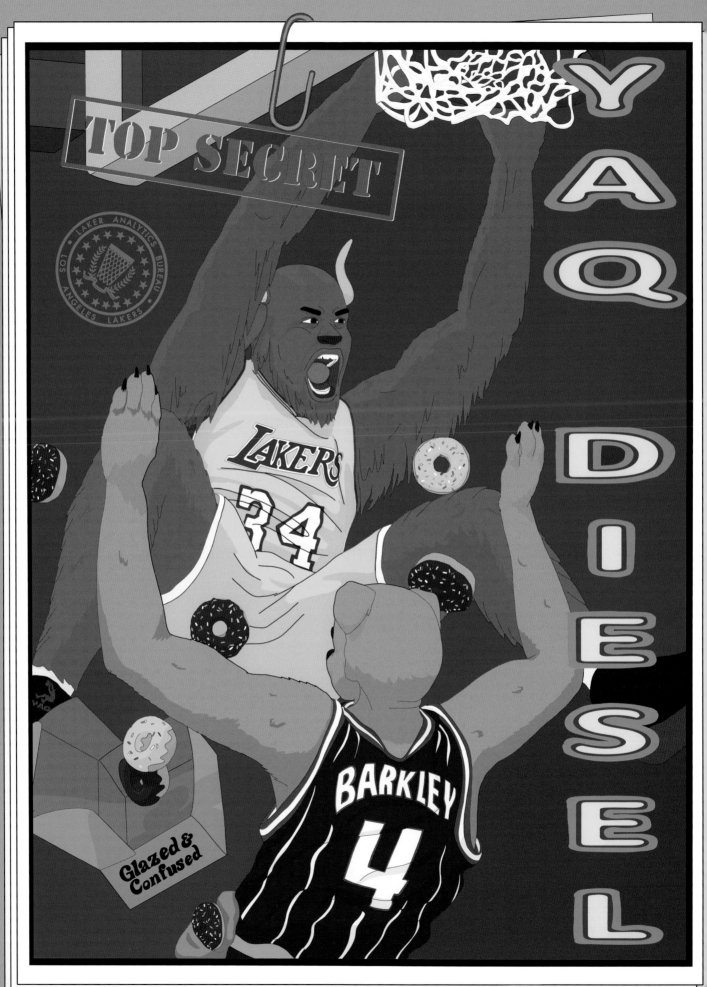

CONFIDENTIAL

YAQUILLE O'NEAL

ALIASES: YAQ DIESEL, SUPER MANE, THE MANE OF STEEL,
THE BIG HAIRYSTOTLE, YAQ DADDY, YAQ FU

Yaquille O'neal aka The Mane of Steel aka The Big Hairy-stotle.

This yak was a basket breaker, a big booty shaker, and a silly nickname

maker. But most of all he was a three-time champion Laker.

Yaq Diesel was **THE. MOST. DOMINANT. EVER.**

CLASSIFIED

DAMIAN LIZARD

PORTLANDIA
0

"YAQ DADDY IS THE DOUBLE GLOAT.
GREATEST LYRICIST OF ALL TIME.
GREATEST LAKER OF ALL TIME."
      -DAMIAN LIZARD

FUN FACTS & JIBBER JABBER:

- Champion, MVP, Finals MVP
- Most feared player & cinematic genie ever
- Greatest free agent signing of all time - 1996
- Made Egg Ostertag say "Uncle" a lot
- Bought Mad Dog Madsen a new car & taught him all his dance moves
- Convinced an entire generation to eat Double Decker Tacos in the 90s

TIME TRAVEL OPTIONS:

1979 – Newark, New Jersey

1986 – Wildflecken, Germany

1987 – Wildflecken, Germany

1988 – San Antonio, Texas

Yaquille O'neal wasn't always dominant. He was tall and clumsy as a teenager in Germany and crushed when he didn't make the high school basketball team TWO YEARS IN A ROW.

The coach picked Hippo Kritt, Bull Oaney & Rhino Plasty for his big guys over Yaq. Not even his buddies Monkey Zunkle, Dingo Barry, or "Moo Money Moo Problems" Milkerson could cheer him up.

 Shaquille O'Neal lived on the US Army base in Wildflecken, Germany for a few years as a teenager while his step-father was stationed there. Do you think he was nervous about moving to a foreign country?

Yaq Diesel was **THIS CLOSE** to quitting basketball and becoming Yakkie Chan, the most dominant Kung Fu Master of all time.

But he didn't give up! He was hungry...

Hungry for tacos! Just kidding. He was hungry to work. Lucky for us he met Chris "Ice" Woodard. Just a normal woodchuck.

The Ice Man picked Yaq for his team when nobody else would. He taught Yaq how to play the game and pretty soon they were beating the other teams on the military base like *a Tribe Called Pest, The Wildebeestie Boys, the Notorious Bee-Eyed-Geese, and Sharky Shark and the Funky Munch*.

 Chris Woodard got cut from his own team in high school. He tried out again as a senior and made it. Then he changed Shaq's life by teaching him how to play in Germany. Normal people can impact the world by helping others!

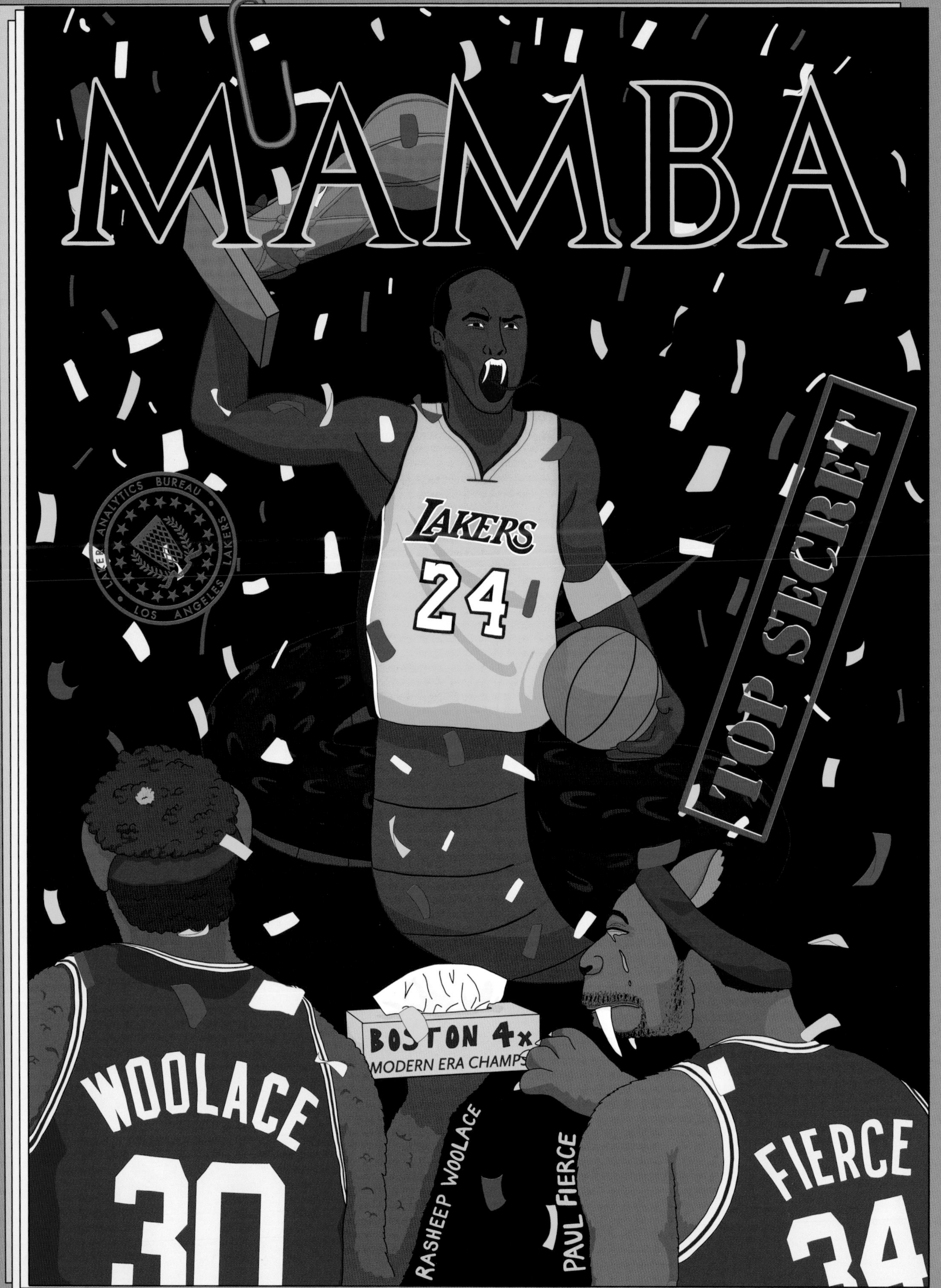
MAMBA
LAKER ANALYTICS BUREAU
LOS ANGELES LAKERS
LAKERS
24
TOP SECRET
BOSTON 4x
MODERN ERA CHAMPS
WOOLACE
30
RASHEEP WOOLACE
PAUL FIERCE
FIERCE
34

LAKER ANALYTICS BUREAU · LOS ANGELES LAKERS

CONFIDENTIAL

KOBE BRYANT

ALIASES: MAMBA, FROBE, VINO, KOBE WAN KENOBI

"MAMBA IS THE GOAT."
-LLAMA ODOM

Kobe Bryant just had that championship sizzle.

He grabbed championship rings like they're hot wings at Sizzler.

With a shot so smooth I Can't Believe It's Not Butter...

No wonder Mamba hit so many shots at the buzzer.

FUN FACTS & JIBBER JABBER:

- Champion, MVP, Finals MVP
- Hardest working player of all time
- Snakes don't have arms, but snake Kobe can have arms if snake Kobe wants to have arms
- Has an actual "Kobe Bryant" day in LA
- Cold blooded. Literally. He's a reptile.
- How cold blooded? Ask Rasheep Woolace, Paul Fierce aka *The Tooth* aka *The Saber Truth Tiger*, Duck Christie, Raja Bull, Matt Barns, Calamari Squidemire, or Smush Barker.

TIME TRAVEL OPTIONS:

1985 – Rieti, Italy

1988 – Pistoia, Italy

1989 – Reggio Emilia, Italy

1992 – Philadelphia, Pennsylvania

"HE BEAT ME IN THE OLYMPICS. THEN HE HUNG HIS GOLD MEDAL IN MY LOCKER FOR MOTIVATION. HE'S THE WORST... AND THE BEST."
-PAU GOOSEOL

Kobe grew up in Italy from age 6 to 13 since his dad played pro basketball there.

He joined in soccer games to make friends while waiting for his basketball court to clear. He played goalie since he was long.

Kobe claims that playing soccer in Italy as a kid helped his basketball. Kobe can speak Italian and Spanish and even used those languages with some foreign teammates as a secret code during games!!

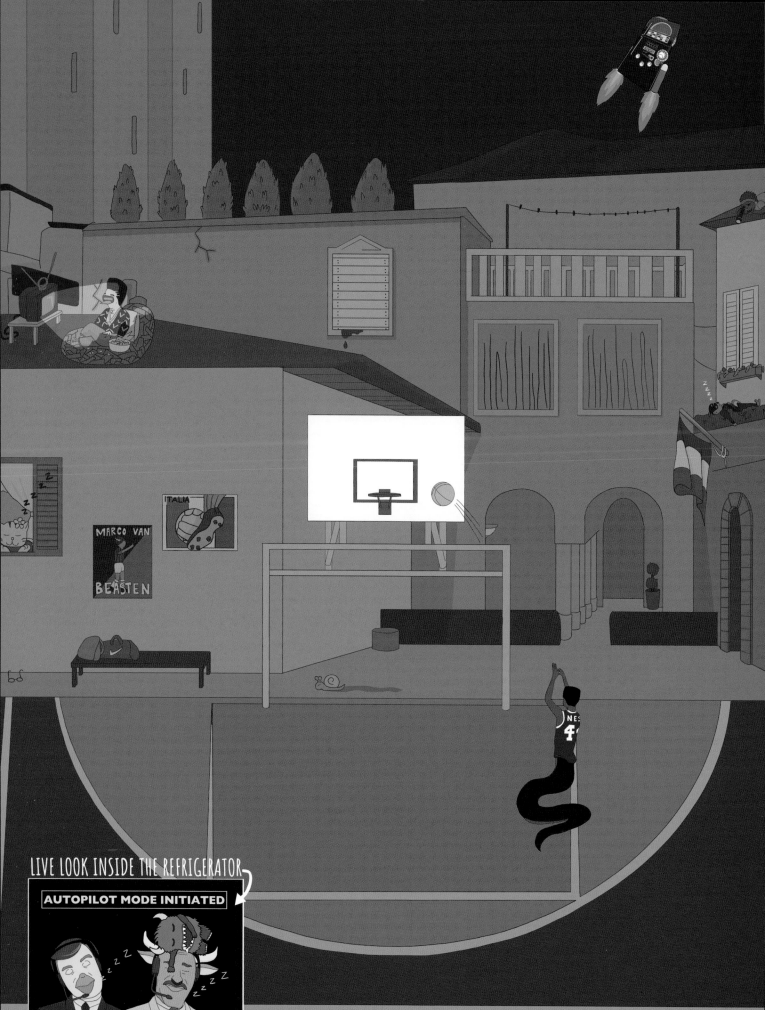

Anytime Kobe started making friends it was time to move again.
He moved to five new cities and schools in seven years!

Italian kids were sometimes afraid of the new kid since he was
different. It was hard being the only black mamba in school.

Working hard helped Kobe get past the lonely times.

 Young Kobe loved the Showtime Lakers as a kid in Italy. His grandpa mailed him tapes of Laker games. He practiced fast breaks like Magic Johnson, runners like James Worthy, and hookshots like Kareem Abdul-Jabbar.

When it was too late to play basketball outside, Kobe continued practicing inside! He would even imagine Chick Hearn and Moo Lantz calling his sock basketball game:

Chick Hearn: *Kobe rolls his dad's sock tight. He slithers back and hits from deep! Nothing but the bottom of the laundry basket on that one, Moo.*

Moo Lantz: *You can smell the detergent from here, Chick. His jumper is CLEAN tonight. Are you calling it, Chick?*

Chick Hearn: *This one's in the Italian refrigerator! The lights are out, the pizza's cooling, the gelato's getting hard, and the panna cotta is jiggling!*

 LIL' MAMBA CHALLENGE: Remember how Kobe moved to five new schools in seven years? Your challenge is to look for new kids who just moved in, sit by them during lunch, and invite them to play during recess. Can you do it?

LEBRON JAMES

ALIASES: KING JAMES, LBJ, CHOSEN ONE, AKRON HAMMER

"I PROMISE SCHOOL" IN HIS HOMETOWN AKRON, OH

LeBron is at the top. He's a champion, MVP, and <u>school maker</u>.

Full time Los Angeles Laker.

Part time Instagram story booty shaker.

As Yak Black would say, he's the beeeeest.

"WE'VE GOT LEBRON AKA LEGOAT!!! YOU ALREADY KNOW WHAT TIME IT IS!!!"
-JUJU SMITH-ROOSTER

FUN FACTS & JIBBER JABBER:

- Champion, MVP, Finals MVP
- King James is not "just a kid from Akron"… he's a really, really giant kid from Akron
- LeBron has a photographic memory – he remembers any play from any game… even in 2008
- <u>Nobody</u> is safe from his camera on Taco Tuesday
- LeBron James is More Than an Athlete - He's a husband, father, friend, school maker, businessman, Space Jam 2 star!, barber shop guy, and taco hype man. Don't try to put him in a box… unless that box also has tacos.

TIME TRAVEL OPTIONS:

1994 – Akron, Ohio

1996 – Akron, Ohio

2003 – Akron, Ohio

2008 – Beijing, China

LeBron remembers being at the bottom. Just him and his mom, Glo' & 'Bron.

No house. No money.

Not knowing what they will eat for dinner on Tuesday.
Not knowing where they will sleep on Wednesday.
Not knowing which school he will go to on Thursday.

 LeBron James never forgot the challenges of living on the brink of homelessness in his hometown as a young child. He helped form the "I Promise School" in Akron, Ohio to help underprivileged children like himself!!!

A few kind coaches changed LeBron's life. Gave him a place to sleep and taught him how to play football and basketball.

LeBron's mom Gloria was so happy that during his football games she would run like crazy along the sidelines when LeBron ran for touchdowns!

 One time his mom was so excited about LeBron's touchdown that she hit his football pads to celebrate and knocked him to the ground!! They went through a lot to get to this point. **After the bitter in life comes the sweet!**

AKRON BACON JOURNAL

75¢

L to R: Sian Cottontail, King James, Blue Joyce III, Rodeo Travis, Woolly McGee

St. INVINCIBLE - St. Mary!

King James is Unstoppable

by Brian Windhorse

Bacon Journal staff writer

It's no secret the struggling Cleveland Calves would love to get LeBron James in the 2003 Draft. Sources are telling Windy that team officials envision a core of King James, Carlos Bluezer, *Dairy*us Miles, Zydrunas Il*goose*kas competing for a playoff spot as early as next year. LeBron has the full arsenal. He passes like Magic and scores like Jordan *as an 18 year old*

WHAT'S THE SQUEAL!?

Weekly Entertainment News from Jerry Swinefeld, Bacon Journal writer

DVDs New to PETFLIX This Month

- Mrs. Snoutfire
- Zoomanji
- Forrest Hump
- Hairy Otter
- Hareborne
- Mean Squirrels
- Encino Manatee
- Flank Check
- Ghost Bustards
- Jingle All the Hay
- The Sixth Scent
- Roam Alone
- Dawson's Beak
- ✱ Ninja Tortoises

- The Princess Bridle
- Udder Cover Brother
- Sheepless in Seattle
- Sixteen Camels
- The Karate Squid
- Butter Off Dead
- Independence Bray
- Yak to the Future
- Moooolan
- Troop Beaverly Hills
- Flight Club
- Saved by the Bull
- Do the Flight Thing
- Indiana Bones

- Where In the World Is Caiman Sandiego?
- Pirates of the Amphibian: Dead Man's Pest
- Bull & Ted's Eggsellent Adventure
- Legends of the Hidden Tadpole
- 10 Things I *Dislike* About Ewe
- Fly Hard: With a Hen-geance
- Ferret Bueller's Day Off
- Angelfish in the Outfield
- Hangin' With Mr. Cougar
- Sabrina the Teenage Ostrich
- Good Wool Hun
- Pinky and th
- The Brea
- Rookie

LeBron worked extremely hard to be the best. Do you know what made him so unique? He worked just as hard to make his teammates the best too! He loved to pass more than score.

 LeBron had a blast winning high school championships with his best friends. This was the beginning of the end for the rest of the basketball world. Good night. Sleep tight. Try not to let King James bite!

CONFIDENTIAL

LAKER ANALYTICS BUREAU · LOS ANGELES LAKERS

ANTHONY DAVIS

ALIASES: THE BROW, AD, THE UNIBURRO, ANT, PHATMAN

Finally Anthony Davis is on the Los Angeles Lakers.

He's always Basket Robbin' since his defense has 31 flavors.

AD. UNIBURRO. ANT. THE BROW.

Better run little chickens or he'll make you Kung Pao.

Unibrows are awesome!!
- Halle Beary

FUTURE IS CLASSIFIED

FUN FACTS & JIBBER JABBER: ~~CLASSIFIED~~

- ~~An~~
- ~~A~~
- Laker Analytics Bureau believes that AD's unibrow is the source of his superpowers on the court
- AD was a really chubby baby so his family called him "Phatman"
- The Brow has a twin sister one minute younger and one foot shorter. She could have a 1 minute, 12 inch growth spurt.
- AD was always LeBron when pretending to be a pro as a kid
- AD's grandpa LOVED Kobe Bryant and told him to work hard to be great like Kobe. AD was destined for the Lakers.

TIME TRAVEL OPTIONS:

- 2006 – Chicago, Illinois
- 2010 – Chicago, Illinois
- 2011 – Lexington, Kentucky
- 2012 – London, England

Penguins were designed for Chicago winters. Not small burros like young Anthony Davis.

AD sold nachos and tickets at basketball games in exchange for a gym key (instead of money!!!) so he could keep practicing in the winter.

 Key to Success! Anthony Davis worked a job for free just for the opportunity to keep working on his game when he was still scrawny & short and people labeled him the "little corner three guy." **AD worked for his greatness.**

AD's dad saw his legs hanging off and wondered if someone shrunk Anthony's bed. Nope! AD GREW 8 INCHES and was now the tallest guy on the team!

Because he worked super hard as the little guy, he was the best player in the ENTIRE COUNTRY once he became the big guy.

"Hey Chick, we've filled all the SWAG canisters," Moo informed. "Let's get these back to Laker Analytics…"

 Thinking Cap! Would Anthony Davis have become the amazing player he is today if he didn't work hard before his growth spurt? What do you think?

Chick and Moo captured the Laker SWAG without the Laker greats noticing and reported back. They completed their mission and SAVED THE WORLD.

There was just one more thing to do...

Chick and Moo took Blorp back to his space monster planet.

"I'm actually going to miss that guy Blorp," Chick confessed.

"Ya know… I think I might as well," Moo agreed.

"But it's nice with just the two of us again," Chick chuckled.

They had no idea what was riding on the back of the time machine…

BLARP!!!

THE END

There's not even .4 seconds left. This thing is over.

Fisher noun

fish·er | \ fi-shər \

1. a dark brown North American carnivorous mammal of the weasel family

2. an absolute baller who hit clutch shot after clutch shot after clutch shot to help the Lakers win five championships

Walrus Hazzard Rudy LaRussell Terrier Bobcat Boozer Gene Woolly Jim King Cobra John Fairchinchil

Bill McGill Duck Barnett Jim Crabs Cottontail Nash Swan Nelson Jerry Goat Frank Shellvy Mule Gibs

Hoppert "Hop" Reed Hot Rod Houndley Howling Jolliff Ron Horn Bobcat McNeill Booby (Bird) Smi

Stingray Felix Wing Yates Gary Owlcorn Prawn Johnson Slick Leopard Boo Walrus Woodchuck Sha

Bob Burrow Duck Garmaker Ed Flamingo Hairy Foust Nick (Praying) Mantis Prawn Sobieszczy

Steve Hamilton Vern Minkkelsen Art Spoelstraw Porky Devlin Duck Schnitzer Clydesdale Lovellet

McCoy Wingram Bobcat Williams Woodchuck Mencel Ed Camelfat Flighty Skoog Jim Paxsongbird, S

Don Thunderbirdcage Otter Dukes George Minkan Jim Holstingray Flew Hitch Ron Ferreteis

Slater Marten Bobcat Carney Jim Polar (Bear) Bobcat Harrison Pup Saul Howling Schultz Joe Hooti

Arnie Ferret Bug Grant Red (Fox) Beach Kevin O'Sheep Tony Jawros Billygoat Hassett Don Snarls

Green Stump Swarmy Glick Paw Walther Dog Smith Donnie Furman Squirrel Gardner Quack Dwe

Hermit Crab Schaefer Johnny Jaguarsen Mink Bloom Stingray Ellfeson Flighty Kachan THANK YOU T

LAKER OWNERSHIP! Dr. Jerry Buzz Jeanie Buzz Janie Buzz Jim Buzz Johnny Buzz Joey Buzz Jesse Buz

Philip Anshoaltz Ed Husky Jr. Dr. Pawtrick Soon-Shiong Dan Beakerman Quack Kent-Cooke Bobcat Sho

THANK YOU TO THE LAKER HEAD COACHES! John Condorla George Minkan John Crabstellani Jim Pole

Fred Sloths Butcher van Breda Kolff Joe Moleaney Bull Sharman Jerry Nest Jack McKennel Paw Westhea

Bat Riley Mink Dunleavy Randy Pfind Bearvin "Magic" Johnson Del Hareis Kurt Rambis Phil Jackals

Kangaroody Tomjanovich Mike Bruin Mink D'Antoni Byron Trot Luke Woolton Frank Vogull THANK YO

TO THE LAKER ASSISTANT COACHES! Lionel Howlins Jason Squid Fowl Handy Mike Penguinberthy Moo

Simon Quinton Clawford Egg St. Jean Chew Anthrop Bull Bertka Frank Hamblen T-Rex Winter Kurt Ramb

Bernie Bickerstag Darvin Ham Mad Dog Madsen Woodchuck Person Quin Spider Steed Clifford Crai

Hogges Bruin Keefe Jelly(fish) Mermuys Chewed Buechler John Cuckooster Cagey Owens Dave Woo

Larry Flew Molevin Hunt Michael Cougar Jim Clammons Camel Abdul-Jabbar James Woolthy Stan Albuc

Eggie Jordan Brian Shaw aka "Bee Shaw" Ettore Mooseina Mice Thibault Jim Aye-Ayen Ed Pulibinsk

Tracy Moray (Eel) Chet Hammerheader Theo Robabirusan Thank you to Laker Health! Gharial Vitti Jud

Stoato Mako (Shark) Nunez Gunnar Beetleson Nignaw Hsieh Mink Mancias Jon Ishopod Stacey Robiso

Octavio Marquez Manateenoya Cheetahn Hill Elk Streit Sandra Parmadillo Thank you Lakers Front Offic

& Org! Jerry Nest Jim Purrrzik Jeanie Buzz Jim Buzz Munch Cubchak Rob Pelincat Tim Hareis Josep

McCormackerel John Black Bear Dan Grizzly Joey Buzz Jesse Buzz Kurt Rambis Eland Shen Janie Buz

Linda Rambis Jordan Woolkes Ryan Nest Nick Muzzlea Nicholas Ligeros Ramdy Mims Kieshark N